characters created by lauren child

please
may I have
SOME of
yours?

PUFFIN

Charlie and Lola ®

Text based on
the script written by
Carol Noble

Illustrations from
the TV animation
produced by Tiger Aspect

PUFFIN BOOKS
Published by the Penguin Group: London, New York, Australia,
Canada, India, Ireland, New Zealand and South Africa
Penguin Books Ltd, Registered Offices: 80 Strand, London WC2R 0RL, England

puffinbooks.com

First published 2011
Published in this edition 2014
001
Text and illustrations copyright © Lauren Child/Tiger Aspect Productions Limited, 2011
The Charlie and Lola logo ® and © Lauren Child, 2005
Charlie and Lola is produced by Tiger Aspect Productions
All rights reserved
The moral right of the author/illustrator has been asserted
Made and printed in China
ISBN: 978-0-141-36037-9

I have this little sister Lola.
She is small and very funny.
Today Lola is really excited because
Granny and Grandpa are taking us both to the zoo.
"I can't wait to see the seals, Charlie. Bark! Bark!"

When we are getting ready, Lola says,
"What are you going to buy from the zoo shop, Charlie?

I'm getting a completely good
seal toy for the bath.
Just like Lotta's!"

And I say,
"I'd really like one of those **books** that shows where all the animals come from."

Charlie

Then I say,
"Lola, you can't eat your **tangerine** now. Mum packed it for lunch. You're not very good at **saving** things for later."

"Yes I am, Charlie."

And I say,
"You are **not!**"

"When you read a
book, you NEVER
wait for the end.
You always skip ahead!"

"Oh no!
Now I know
what **happens**."

In the car on the way to the zoo, I say,
"Maybe you shouldn't eat your **sandwich** now, Lola.
You should save it for later."

But Lola just says,
"Charlie, what is this box?"

"It's a **camera**. Dad bought some for
us so we can take pictures of
all the animals at the **zoo**."

Granny and Grandpa stop at the park so Lola and I can feed the **ducks**.

I break off little pieces of bread, but Lola throws all of hers straight into the pond.

Lola says,
"I've run out of bread, Charlie.
Please may I have
some of **yours**?"

I say,
"All right, Lola."

When we get to the **zoo**, Granny and Grandpa say we can look at any animal we want.

I say,
"Lola! Look at the **giraffes!**"

"Ooh, they're especially good," says Lola. "But my clicky **camera** is completely full up, Charlie. **Please** can I borrow **yours**?"

Click!

Click!

And I say, "OK, Lola. But just take one photo because I really want to photograph the **anteaters** and the **armadillos**."

Click!

Then Lola says,
      "I'm going to
ask Granny if I can
      buy a z**oo** balloon!"

And I say,
"Don't you think you should
            save your **pocket money**
      if you want to buy your
seal toy at the **zoo** shop later?"

"But I've got **lots** of money, Charlie," says Lola.

At lunchtime, Lola says,
"Charlie, please can I have some of your sandwich?"

"But Lola... you've already had yours."

"Please, Charlie."

I say,
"You can have a little bit."

Lola says,
    "I am going to buy
some pink milk because I
    really am extremely thirsty."

I say,
    "Lola, you won't have
anything left to spend in the
    zoo shop."

"Oh yes I will, Charlie.
    I still have
    one more bit of money."

When we get to the **seal** tank,
Lola says, "Oooh. Bark! Bark!
Can I **please** borrow your **camera**, Charlie?
I absolutely must take a
photograph of the **seals**."

"Yes," I say.

"But you can only take ONE photo because I'm saving them for the **armadillos**."

Click!

Click!

Click!

"Lola!!"

"Oops! Sorry, Charlie. I used it up by **accident**."

At the **zoo** shop, Lola says,
"Now I must go and find my **seal** toy."

And I say,
"Look, Lola. This is The Complete Animal Atlas.
It has all the animals
and where they come from..."

There's an **elephant**,

an **armadillo**

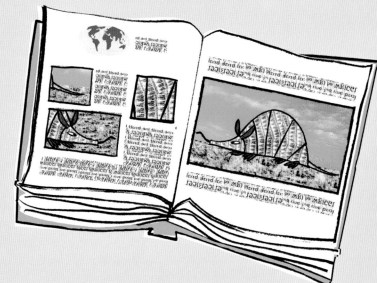

and a bald **eagle**!"

But Lola isn't listening.
Instead she says,
    "The man said I didn't have enough
moneч for my seal toy."

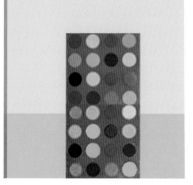

I say,
    "That's because you spent
your **pocket money** on all
        those other things."

Lola says,
    "But what will I do now, Charlie?
Now I won't have a toy like Lotta's."

So I say,
"Here you are, Lola.
You can have some
of MY money."

And Lola says,
"Oh, thank you
ever so
much,
Charlie."

On the way home, Lola says,
  "Are there any seals in your animal book, Charlie?"

And I say,
"I didn't buy the
book because I didn't
have enough money."

Lola says,
"I thought you had lots
of m**o**n**e**y because you
saved it up."

"No, Lola," I say.
"I didn't have enough
for my **book** after
I gave you the
money for the
seal toy."

The next day Lola starts
to save things up.

And she doesn't skip
to the end of her
book any more.

Whenever we get
pocket money,
Lola puts hers
straight into
her **piggy bank**.

"I'll save
       this for later.

And one of these.

                And this."

When we go to the **duck** pond, Lola only uses
a little bit of her bread.
And she even gives some to me.

I say,

"Thanks, Lola. I've nearly saved up
enough **pocket money** to buy an
animal **atlas**. When Dad takes
us to the **bookshop**, I'm definitely
going to buy it."

And Lola says,
"I've been saving up, too,
Charlie. I might buy a
book about seals.
Bark! Bark!"

At the **bookshop**, I say,
"Oh no. This costs more than the
book in the **zoo** shop.
I haven't got enough **money**!"

"Don't worry, Charlie," says Lola.
"You can have some of MY pocket money
because I've saved lots."

"Thank you, Lola,"
I say.

Then I say, "Ugh, what's that in your pocket, Lola?"

"It's my tangerine, Charlie.
I've been saving it up
　　　just in case we need a snack!"